STAR WARS® TALES

Volume 1

DARK HORSE BOOKS™

STAR WARS TALES

CONTENTS

Publisher / Mike Richardson
Editor / Dave Land
Assistant Editor / Philip Simon
Collection Designer / Lia Ribacchi
Art Director / Mark Cox

Special thanks to
Lucy Autrey Wilson and Chris Cerasi
at Lucas Licensing

STAR WARS®: TALES — VOLUME 1

This book collects issues 1 through 4 of the Dark Horse quarterly comic-book anthology Star Wars®: Tales.

Dark Horse Books™
A division of Dark Horse Comics, Inc.
10956 SE Main Street
Milwaukie, OR 97222

www.darkhorse.com
www.starwars.com

Comic Shop Locator Service: (888) 266-4226

First edition: January 2002
ISBN: 1-56971-619-6

7 9 10 8 6
Printed in China

I...

...I DIDN'T KNOW YOU WERE ON CORUSCANT, L-LUH...

ONE HAS BEEN *FOUND.*

HOW, MASTER? I HAVE ELIMINATED *MANY,* BUT MY SEARCHES HAVE YIELDED NO MORE.

YOUR SEARCHES, YES.

HOWEVER, THE *PAWNS* AT MY DISPOSAL ARE NUMEROUS.

THERE ARE *OTHERS* WHO SERVE MY NEEDS.

RUN ALONG NOW. THIS ISN'T GOING TO BE ANY PLACE FOR *YOU* TO BE.

SO FEW *EXIST* ANYMORE. I'VE BEEN KEEPING IT ALIVE *NURTURING* IT, UNTIL IT CAN SPREAD AGAIN.

ONE MUST BE PATIENT. *WEEDS* APPEAR FROM TIME TO TIME, THREATENING TO CHOKE OUT SUCH BLOSSOMS.

EXTINCTION IS THE NATURAL ORDER OF THINGS.

WEAKER SPECIES ARE REPLACED BY STRONGER ONES.

CERTAIN SPECIES ARE *HEARTIER* THAN YOU SUSPECT. THEY *BIDE* THEIR TIME...

...IN PLACES LIKE THIS. AND *BLOOM* WHEN YOU LEAST EXPECT IT.

END

Senshi / ART BY TSUNEO SANDA

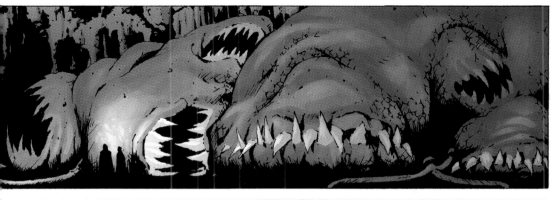

IT'S DONE. LET'S LEAVE.

MASTER... MAY I ASK A QUESTION?

OF COURSE, OBI-WAN.

DID WE TRULY DO THE RIGHT THING BY KILLING THE SILAN? IT FELT SO AWFUL TO TAKE SUCH A *LARGE* LIFE.

IT WAS UNPLEASANT FOR ME, TOO.

BUT WE ARE *JEDI*. OUR LIVES ARE NOT OURS TO LIVE AS WE WISH. WE ARE PLEDGED TO SERVE A HIGHER POWER THAN OURSELVES.

BUT...IT FELT *WRONG* TO ME. I THOUGHT SERVING THE LIVING FORCE MEANT HAVING RESPECT FOR *ALL CREATURES*...

...THE SILAN HAD ITS PLACE IN THE NATURAL SCHEME OF THINGS, DIDN'T IT?

IT ONLY DID AS ITS NATURE TOLD IT TO DO. WHAT RIGHT HAD WE TO SEEK IT OUT AND *DESTROY* IT? IT WASN'T *HARMING* US.

THE WAYS OF THE LIVING FORCE ARE BEYOND OUR UNDERSTANDING.

WHO KNOWS WHY WE WERE DIRECTED TO EXTERMINATE THAT BEAST: PERHAPS WE WERE AGENTS OF RETRIBUTION. PERHAPS PERFORMED AN ACT OF LIBERATION. WE CANNOT KNOW...WE CAN ONLY SERVE.

AS A JEDI KNIGHT YOU WILL BE CALLED UPON TO DO MANY THINGS YOU DON'T WANT TO DO, OBI-WAN.

OUR PATH IS NOT AN EASY ONE TO FOLLOW.

BUT FEAR NOT. YOU ARE IN THE HANDS OF SOMETHING MUCH GREATER AND MUCH BETTER THAN YOU CAN IMAGINE.

THE END

ON THE DESOLATE WORLD OF TATOOINE, OBI-WAN KENOBI KNEW THERE WERE TWO POTENTIAL JEDI KNIGHTS LEFT. ONE, HE KNEW, WAS LUKE SKYWALKER, SON OF ANAKIN.

THE OTHER, HOWEVER, OBI-WAN COULD NOT PINPOINT. IT WAS TREMENDOUSLY *FRUSTRATING* FOR KENOBI. LONG DID HE SEARCH THROUGHOUT TATOOINE, THROUGH AN ASSORTMENT OF WRETCHED HIVES OF SCUM AND VILLAINY...

THROUGH NAUSEATING ENCLAVES OF LOATHING AND DEPRAVITY...

...AND THROUGH MANY *OTHER* PLACES OF EQUALLY TORTURED SYNTAX.

THERE WERE TIMES WHEN HE FELT THAT HE WAS ALMOST ON TOP OF HIM, BUT HE WOULD LOOK AROUND, CHECK THE CROWDS OF ALIEN BEINGS ALL AROUND HIM, AND WAS UNABLE--FOR ALL HIS POWERS OF THE FORCE--TO *LOCATE* HIM.

LITTLE DID HE SUSPECT THAT THE MYSTERIOUS JEDI WAS LITERALLY UNDER HIS NOSE. FOR THE ONE HE WAS SEARCHING FOR WAS...

SKIPPY
THE JEDI DROID

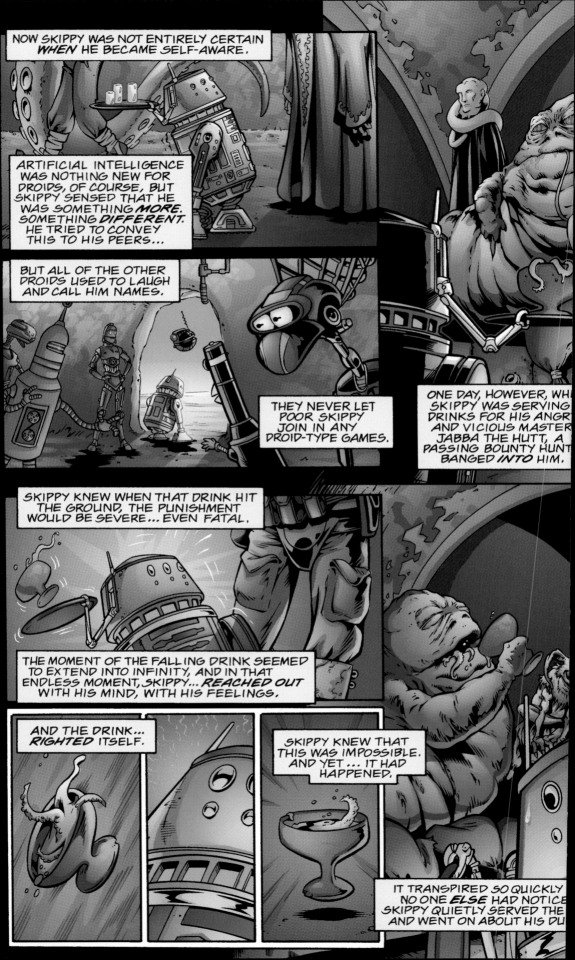

NOW SKIPPY WAS NOT ENTIRELY CERTAIN *WHEN* HE BECAME SELF-AWARE.

ARTIFICIAL INTELLIGENCE WAS NOTHING NEW FOR DROIDS, OF COURSE, BUT SKIPPY SENSED THAT HE WAS SOMETHING *MORE*. SOMETHING *DIFFERENT*. HE TRIED TO CONVEY THIS TO HIS PEERS...

BUT ALL OF THE OTHER DROIDS USED TO LAUGH AND CALL HIM NAMES.

THEY NEVER LET POOR SKIPPY JOIN IN ANY DROID-TYPE GAMES.

ONE DAY, HOWEVER, WH[EN] SKIPPY WAS SERVING DRINKS FOR HIS ANGR[Y] AND VICIOUS MASTER JABBA THE HUTT, A PASSING BOUNTY HUNT[ER] BANGED *INTO* HIM.

SKIPPY KNEW WHEN THAT DRINK HIT THE GROUND, THE PUNISHMENT WOULD BE SEVERE... EVEN FATAL.

THE MOMENT OF THE FALLING DRINK SEEMED TO EXTEND INTO INFINITY, AND IN THAT ENDLESS MOMENT, SKIPPY... *REACHED OUT* WITH HIS MIND, WITH HIS FEELINGS.

AND THE DRINK... *RIGHTED* ITSELF.

SKIPPY KNEW THAT THIS WAS IMPOSSIBLE. AND YET... IT HAD HAPPENED.

IT TRANSPIRED SO QUICKLY NO ONE *ELSE* HAD NOTICE[D] SKIPPY QUIETLY SERVED THE [DRINK] AND WENT ON ABOUT HIS DU[TIES]

THAT NIGHT, WHILE EVERYONE [SL]EEPING, HE TRIED TO MOVE [SOME]THING. NOTHING MAJOR, JUST A *ROCK.*

[N]OTHING HAPPENED AT FIRST, BUT THEN...

SKIPPY PRACTICED *NIGHTLY.* HE HAD NO IDEA WHAT WAS HAPPENING; HE ONLY KNEW THAT HE POSSESSED SOME SORT OF BIZARRE SKILL, LIKE THE FABLED JEDI KNIGHTS...

[H]IS LUBRICANTS [WE]RE RIFE WITH ['CH]LOROXIANS,' [GIVING] HIM MASTERY [OF] THE FORCE.

AND ONE NIGHT, ONE AMAZING NIGHT... SKIPPY *ESCAPED.* WITH HIS AMAZING POWER, HE REMOVED HIS RESTRAINING BOLT.

[TH]E TWO MASSIVE GUARDS [B]ARRED HIS WAY, BUT [SKI]PPY SIMPLY REACHED [OUT] WITH THE POWER OF [TH]E FORCE AND SAID...

BEEP A BEEP DOO BOP BOP.

...WHICH TRANSLATED MEANS, "I'M NOT THE DROID YOU'RE LOOKING FOR."

AND SKIPPY ROLLED TO FREEDOM. FREEDOM TO SEEK HIS DESTINY AS A JEDI DROID.

THERE WAS, HOWEVER, A PROBLEM WHICH SKIPPY NOW HAD TO *FACE.*

HE WAS IN THE MIDDLE OF A DESERT... NOT SURPRISING, SINCE *ALL* OF TATOOINE IS A DESERT.

JEDI OR NOT, DROID OR NOT, BEING IN A DESERT CAN BE AN INTIMIDATING AND DAUNTING PROSPECT.

(ALTHOUGH NO MATTER HOW HARD HE TRIED, HE COULD NOT HIDE FROM THE FACT THAT BINARY STARS HAVE NO PLANETS DUE TO THEIR MASSIVE GRAVITY WELLS, BUT WE WON'T GET INTO THAT.)

HE HID FROM THE SAND PEOPLE FROM TUSKEN.

BY DAY HE HID IN SHADOWS FROM THE TWIN SUNS OF TATOOINE...

BUT POOR SKIPPY BEGAN TO WEAR DOWN. HE BECAME FILTHY, ENCRUSTED WITH DIRT, SAND WORKING INTO HIS INNARDS.

AND THEN, ONE DAY, HIS DESTINY FOUND HIM.

HIS POWER CELLS WERE DRAINING, AND SLOWLY HE CAME TO REALIZE THAT, EVEN THOUGH HE WAS A DROID OF DESTINY, IT MIGHT BE THAT HE DIDN'T HAVE THE OPPORTUNITY TO FIND IT.

UNDER ORDINARY CIRCUMSTANCES, HE WOULD HAVE ENDEAVORED TO HIDE FROM THE JAWAS. BUT HE KNEW HE HAD LITTLE CHOICE. HE WASN'T GOING TO BE ABLE TO LAST MUCH LONGER ON HIS OWN.

SO SKIPPY LET THE JAWAS SPOT HIM. THEY CLEANED HIM UP AS BEST THEY COULD.

AND SKIPPY DECIDED THAT HE WOULD STAY ABOARD THE TRANSPORT FOR A WHILE, KNOWING HE COULD ESCAPE ANY TIME.

AND THEN ONE DAY HE MET TWO DROIDS. ONE WAS ANOTHER R2 UNIT. BUT THIS R2 UNIT SEEMED OBSESSED WITH SOME SORT OF *MISSION*... A MESSAGE TO BE DELIVERED TO AN "OBI-WAN KENOBI."

THE NAME STRUCK A CHORD WITHIN SKIPPY. HE SENSED THAT THE FORCE WAS TRYING TO TELL HIM SOMETHING, BUT SKIPPY WAS SORELY FRUSTRATED AND WAS UNABLE TO COMPREHEND.

THEN *ANOTHER* DROID SHOWED UP. THIS ONE WAS CALLED C-3PO, AND HE WOULDN'T SHUT UP.

HIS YAMMERING MADE IT DIFFICULT FOR SKIPPY TO CONCENTRATE ON THE SENSE OF THE FUTURE HE WAS BEGINNING TO HAVE. THERE WERE IMAGES SWIRLING IN HIM HE COULD NOT QUITE *UNDERSTAND*.

A VISION OF A MAN DRESSED IN BLACK, AND OF A YOUNG WOMAN WHO, FOR SOME REASON, HAD *CINNAMON ROLLS* ON HER HEAD.

AND ARMORED SOLDIERS, AND SOMETIMES THEY WERE RIDING ON LARGE LIZARD-LIKE CREATURES, BUT OTHER TIMES THEY WERE JUST SITTING ON A LARGE *REPLICA* OF ONE. IT WAS ALL VERY CONFUSING.

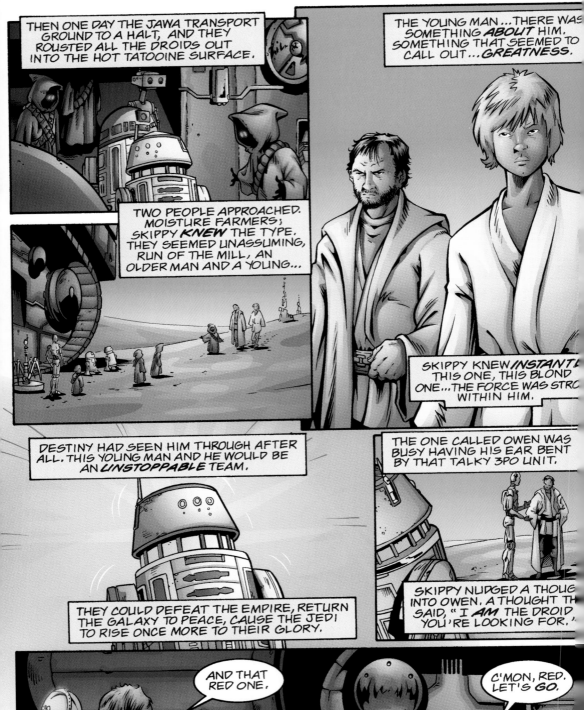

THEN ONE DAY THE JAWA TRANSPORT GROUND TO A HALT, AND THEY ROUSTED ALL THE DROIDS OUT INTO THE HOT TATOOINE SURFACE.

TWO PEOPLE APPROACHED. MOISTURE FARMERS; SKIPPY *KNEW* THE TYPE. THEY SEEMED UNASSUMING, RUN OF THE MILL, AN OLDER MAN AND A YOUNG...

THE YOUNG MAN...THERE WAS SOMETHING *ABOUT* HIM, SOMETHING THAT SEEMED TO CALL OUT...*GREATNESS*.

SKIPPY KNEW *INSTANTL* THIS ONE, THIS BLOND ONE...THE FORCE WAS STR WITHIN HIM.

DESTINY HAD SEEN HIM THROUGH AFTER ALL. THIS YOUNG MAN AND HE WOULD BE AN *UNSTOPPABLE* TEAM.

THEY COULD DEFEAT THE EMPIRE, RETURN THE GALAXY TO PEACE, CAUSE THE JEDI TO RISE ONCE MORE TO THEIR GLORY.

THE ONE CALLED OWEN WAS BUSY HAVING HIS EAR BENT BY THAT TALKY 3PO UNIT.

SKIPPY NUDGED A THOUG INTO OWEN, A THOUGHT TH SAID, " I *AM* THE DROID YOU'RE LOOKING FOR,"

AND THAT RED ONE.

C'MON, RED. LET'S *GO*.

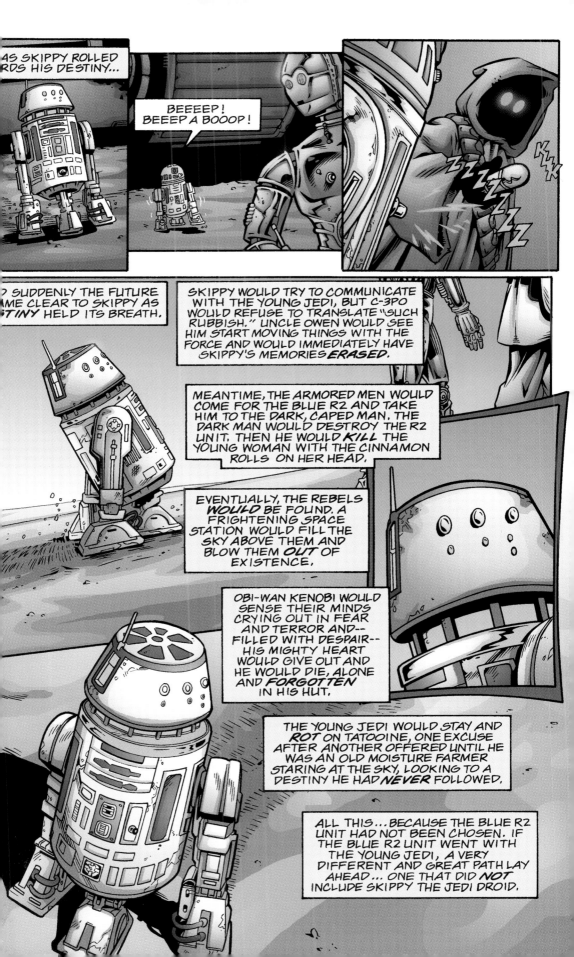

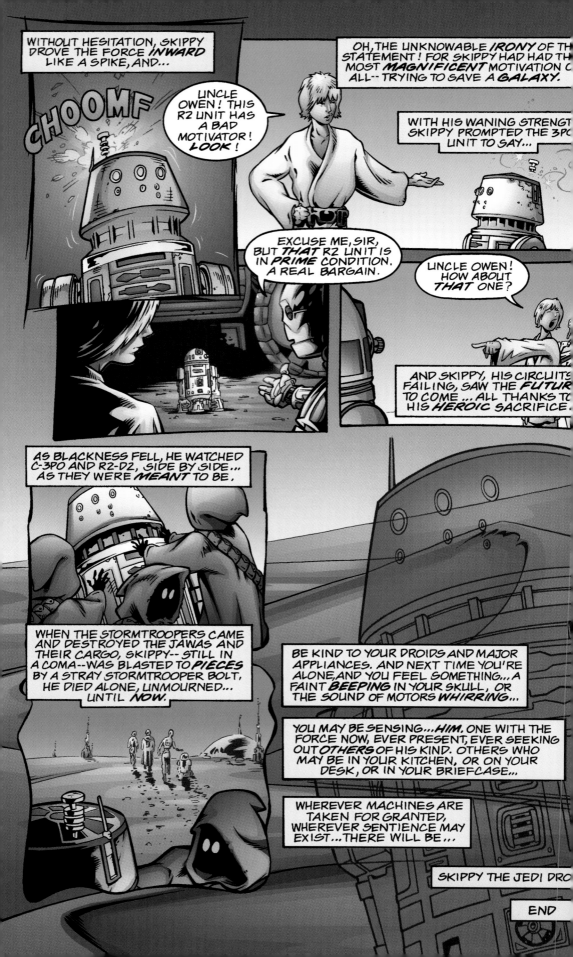

"I REMEMBER THE *EMPEROR* POINTING HIM OUT TO ME ONCE. A VERY POPULAR MAN, THEN, AND STILL ON THE RISE."

AND IF MADINE THINKS THE *EMPIRE'S* GOING TO LET HIM SIT OUT THE WAR IN SOME REBEL PRISON CELL, THEY'D BETTER THINK HARDER,

WHERE TO?

I DON'T KNOW THE ADDRESS--I WAS ONLY THER *ONCE.* BUT I CAN DIRECT YOU

THIS IS IT, RIGHT HERE, THANKS,

SURE, STAY DRY, NOW,

RIGHT,

I WOULDN'T HAVE THOUGHT A COLONY TH SMALL WOULD HAVE A IMPERIAL GARRISON OBVIOUS PLACE FOR THE REBELS TO SET SHOP, THOUGH,

I SUPPOSE I COULD GO OVER AND ANNOUNCE MYSELF, BUT THAT PROBABLY WOULDN'T DO WONDERS FOR MY LIFE EXPECTANCY, BETTER LOOK FOR A BACK DOOR FIRST,

MY *FORCE* SKILLS HAVE BEEN FADING EVE SINCE *SKYWALKER* AND *VADER* MURDERED TH EMPEROR. BUT I SHOULD HAVE ENOUGH LEFT...

AH--THE REWARDS OF PATIENCE. AND THEY WERE EVEN KIND ENOUGH TO LEAVE ME A *GUARD DROID* TO DEAL WITH INSTEAD OF LIVE TROOPERS,

PROBABLY COULDN'T FIND ANYONE WILLING TO STAND WATCH OUT HERE IN THE RAIN,

THE GAP LOOKS PRETTY NARROW. I'LL WANT TO CHECK IT OUT BEFORE I COMMIT MYSELF,

AMAZING--THE GUARDS ON THE ARMORY ACTUALLY LOOK HALFWAY ALERT, FIRST ONES I'VE SEEN HERE YET THAT DID.

CAN'T CUT MY WAY IN FROM THE SIDE--THE ARMORY WILL HAVE THE SAME EMBEDDED SECURITY MESH AS THE OUTER WALL, AND I DON'T HAVE THE EQUIPMENT TO JUMP THE WIRES.

TOO BAD, THOUGH--IT WOULD HAVE BEEN EASIER IF THEY'D BEEN ASLEEP. STILL, YOU CAN'T EXPECT EVEN REBELS TO BE STUPID ALL THE TIME.

I WONDER IF I'VE STILL GOT ENOUGH FORCE STRENG LEFT TO CREATE A SMALL NO

WEEOOWOO

I GUESS SO. COME ON, GENTLEMEN, GIVE ME THREE MORE SECONDS...

THANK YOU.

GOT TO MOVE FAST-- THERE'LL BE OTHERS INSIDE, AND THEY MAY HAVE HEARD THE COMMOTION.

THERE ARE GOING TO BE A LOT OF HEADACHES AROUND HER WHEN THESE GUYS WAKE UP. NO TO COLLECT THE NECESSARY GOO AND GET MOVING.

AND HOPE THERE'S NO GUAR CHANGE SCHEDULE FOR THE NEXT HALF-HOUR.

EITHER EVERYONE'S EADY ASLEEP, OR THIS ACE IS *SEVERELY* RMANNED. EITHER WAY, GOING TO MAKE LIFE A LOT SIMPLER.

GETTING HIM OUT OF THE ROOM WILL BE EASY ENOUGH. GETTING HIM OUT OF THE *BUILDING* WILL BE A BIT TRICKIER.

IMPRESSIVE LONG-RANGE COMM/ SENSOR NEXUS. PROBABLY EXPLAINS WHY THERE WAS A GARRISON HERE.

RECORDS FILES SHOULD BE IN *THAT* ROOM. COME ON, *DATAPAD*--LET'S GO FOR A LITTLE WALK.

I'D BETTER TRY TO SHIFT THE ODDS A LITTLE.

I JUST HOPE THE LAST *FLEET* FLYBY WASN'T TOO LONG AGO.

OKAY, I'M WIRED IN. SEARCHING RECORDS...

I'LL BE BLINKED-- THAT'S THE *EXECUTOR*. WHAT IN SPACE WAS *VADER* DOING WAY OUT HERE?

DOESN'T MATTER. MAKE A QUICK COPY OF THE RECORD...

...LINK IT INTO THE MAIN SENSOR FEED...

..., AND THE STAGE IS *SET*. NOW LET'S SEE IF I CAN ARRANGE FOR A FEW *SOUND EFFECTS*.

SO FAR, SO GOOD.

EITHER THESE GUYS ARE LESS IMPRESSIVE THAN EVEN THE AVERAGE REBEL, OR THEY JUST WEREN'T EXPECTING COMPANY TONIGHT.

OR ELSE I'M A LOT BETTER AT THIS THAN I THOUGHT.

ZZZZT!

BUT EVEN RIDICULOUS LUCK SHOULDN'T BE PUSHED TOO HARD.

AND TRYING TO TAKE OUT ANOTHER SET OF GUARDS WOULD DEFINITELY BE PUSHING IT.

BUT THIS ROOM SHOULD BE DIRECTLY BEHIND BARKALE'S, ALL I NEED TO DO--

UH--

EITHER REBEL DISCIPLINE DOESN'T EXTEND TO MAKING THEIR BEDS, OR ELSE THIS ROOM HAS HAD A VERY *RECENT* OCCUPANT.

PROBABLY IN THE *'FRESHER.*

I'LL SET FOR STUN, THOUGH UNDER THE CIRCUMSTANCES HE MIGHT PREFER THAT I JUST KILLED HIM.

THAT'S FAR *ENOUGH.*

DROP'EM.

THE CHARGE IS TREASONOUS EMBEZZLEMENT, HAVE YOU ANYTHING TO SAY IN YOUR DEFENSE?

WAIT A MINUTE-- JUST A MINUTE, NOW, I DON'T KNOW WHAT RUMORS YOU'VE BEEN LISTENING TO--

IN THE EMPEROR'S OFFICE,

NO RUMORS, GOVERNOR, I READ YOUR REPORTS MYSELF.

WHAT? BUT--

ALL OF IT-- YOU CAN HAVE ALL OF IT, THERE'S BILLIONS HERE, BILLIONS!

UNGH!

YOU CAME TO HIS ATTENTION MONTHS AGO, YOU, AND YOUR SECTOR'S MYSTERIOUSLY VANISHING FUNDS,

HE ASKED ME TO LOOK INTO IT, BUT I NEVER HAD THE CHANCE TO DO MORE IN SOME PRELIMINARY RECORD SEARCHES, UNTIL NOW.

THE SENTENCE IS DEATH, TO BE CARRIED OUT--

ALL I ASK IS THAT YOU LET ME--

AT THE IMPERIAL ACADEMY, THE CAPTAIN HAD ENVISIONED HIS FUTURE SERVICE MUCH *DIFFERENTLY.*

HE HAD PICTURED HIMSELF AS A GREAT *WARRIOR,* BATTLING THE ENEMIES OF THE EMPEROR--

--AND CONQUERING *WORLDS* IN HIS NAME,

...STEAD, HIS PATH HAD ...ED HIM TO *THIS* ...IGNIFICANT POSTING, ... DAZZLING ASPIRATIONS OF HIS *YOUTH*--

...GIVEN WAY TO THE HARSH ...REALITY OF A MAN GROWN ...LD IN MENIAL SERVICE TO HIS MASTERS,

LITTLE MORE THAN A GALACTIC *CUSTOMS* AGENT,

INSTRUCT ITS *CAPTAIN* TO IDENTIFY HIMSELF AND HIS SHIP AND TO PREPARE TO BE BOARDED FOR A ROUTINE *INSPECTION,*

I'LL BE *JOINING* YOU THIS TIME, RAPRICE,

I FEEL THE NEED TO STRETCH MY *LEGS.*

CAPTAIN! A MID-SIZED VESSEL HAS ENTERED OUR *PATROL* COORDINATES, FROM THE READINGS--

--I'D SAY SHE WAS A CORELLIAN *CORVETTE.*

AS YOU WISH, SIR, THE VESSEL *IS* CORELLIAN, EN ROUTE TO NADIEM, A SMALLISH FARMING COLONY ON THE RIM,

THE SHIP IS REGISTERED AS *JAINA'S LIGHT,* THE CAPTAIN SAYS IT'S NAMED FOR HIS *MOTHER.*

HIS NAME IS *HAN SOLO.*

"A LEVEL ONE INSPECTION HAS BEEN *COMPLETED,* SIR, WE FOUND NOTHING MORE THAN THE GRAIN, SEED, AND GARISH TRINKETS SHOWN ON THE CARGO *MANIFEST.*

"HOWEVER, GIVEN CAPT SOLO'S RATHER *UNUSL* CHOICE FOR A FIRST MAT

--I AM REQUESTING PERMISSION TO INITIATE A LEVEL *TWO* SEARCH OF THIS VESSEL,

THAT *WON'T* BE NECESSARY, LIEUTENANT, I'M SATISFIED WITH YOUR FINDINGS... OR *LACK* THEREOF.

RETURN TO THE *VIGILANT* WITH YOUR TEAM, I'LL BE ALONG IN A *MOMENT* OR TWO,

GRONK

BUT, CAPTAIN, I STILL THINK...

GRUNK.KK

I CERTAINLY *HOPE* SO THOUGH I UNDERSTAND DOUBTS, YOU'RE QUITE YO TO BE IN COMMAND OF THIS VESSEL--

VERY WELL, SIR,

HE DOESN'T SEEM TO *LIKE* ME, DID I DO OR SAY SOMETHING TO *OFFEND* HIM?

--AND *WOOKIEES* ARE MOST UNCOMMON HERE,

WHAT CAN I SAY? THEY WORK *CHEAP.* A GUY LIKE ME NEEDS TO SQUEEZE *EVERY* CREDIT TO MAKE ENDS MEET, ESPECIALLY CARRYING *THIS* KIND OF CARGO,

BUT IT WAS THE FARMERS ON *NADIEM* WHO LOANE ME THE MONEY TO BUY THIS SHIP... IN EXCHANGE FOR MY MAKING THESE PIDDLING LITTLE RUN FOR THEM,

ALL RIGHT, GOT A NEW STABILIZER COMIN' IN DAY AFTER TOMORROW-- YOU'RE LUCKY, THERE, SUPPLY ONLY COMES ONCE A MONTH--

-- BUT IT'LL RUN YOU A GOOD 1400. FIGURE IN LABOR, AND I CAN POINT YOU TO A PLACE TO STAY, WON'T GOUGE YOU *TOO* BAD--

-- PLUS *TRIBUTE*... YOU'RE LOOKIN' AT A GOOD 2600.

T-TRIBUTE?

N'T WORRY NONE OUT TRIBUTE... WON'T BE HERE NG ENOUGH R IT TO CAUSE NO TROUBLE. N YOU DO THE 2600?

B-B-*BARELY.* GREAT! THIS WIPES OUT MY WH-WHOLE LAST RUN!

HEY, LIFE'S TOUGH.

Y-Y-YEAH. SO... uh, WH-WHAT IS THERE TO D-D-

-DO AROUND HERE FOR TWO DAYS?

HI THERE, STRANGER!

WHOA, HEY, I'M NOT GONNA *BITE* YOU. RELAX.

IT'S JUST, NOT MANY HUMANS COME THROUGH HERE... NOT MUCH CALL FOR HUMAN COMPANY, Y'KNOW?

MY NAME'S *KIRRY*. I THOUGHT YOU MIGHT LIKE TO *TALK* A BIT.

I-I-I'M NOT MUCH FOR T-TALKING... ESPECIALLY NOT T-TONIGHT--

HEY! HEY *YOU!* HUMAN!

GIVE ME SOME *MONEY!* I *KNOW* YOU'VE GOT SOME! *GIVE ME SOME MONEY!*

I-I-I-

MY *GOSH!* I'VE NEVER SEEN *ANYONE* MOVE THAT *FAST* BEFORE, ARE YOU A PROFESSIONAL?

YEAH, HE'S ALIVE. GET HIM *OUT* OF HERE!

―WHAT?

PROFESSIONAL, ARE YOU A PROFESSIONAL BLASTFIGHTER?

N-N-*NO!*

I-I-I'M A *ROCK MINER!* JUST A... JUST A ROCK MINER...

I-I'VE *NEVER*... I D-DIDN'T... I WASN'T EVEN SURE THE G-*GUN* WOULD WORK...

EXCUSE ME, SIR...

WE EXTEND TO YOU AN INVITATION FROM HIS LORD AND MASTER, SHOTO EYEFIRE, TO PARTICIPATE IN A CONTEST OF REFLEXES AND ACCURACY, AS DEMONSTRATED THROUGH THE USE OF FIREARMS.

THIS CONTEST WILL BE HELD TOMORROW, JUST AFTER SUNRISE. WE WILL COME FOR YOU.

OH, NO... OH, NO...

I WAS GOING TO THROW YOU OUT OF MY BAR...

... BUT YOU'LL BE DEAD THIS TIME TOMORROW, SO HERE'S ONE ON THE HOUSE.

WAS A FAIR SHOOTING, ANYWAY.

Uh... K-KIRRY? WH-WH-WH-WHAT WAS HE T-TALKING ABOUT? WHO'S THIS SH-SHOTO?

C'MON, I'LL SHOW YOU.

THAT'S SHOTO'S PLACE. HIS FORTRESS. IT'D TAKE AN ARMY JUST TO GET INTO IT.

NOT THAT ANYBODY HERE WOULD EVER TRY. HE CONTROLS HORN STATION. SHOWED UP ABOUT TEN YEARS AGO, AND TOOK OVER.

"B-BUT, WHAT'S THIS C-CONTEST?"

"WELL, SHOTO IS A BLASTFIGHTER, FASTEST AROUND HERE, AND HE'S ALREADY KILLED ALL THE LOCAL COMPETITION, SO NOW HE LOOKS OUT FOR NEW PROSPECTS...

...AND THAT'S YOU."

"B-BUT-- BUT WHAT IF I-- IF I JUST *LEAVE?* R-REFUSE THIS I-INVITATION?"

"LEAVE *HOW?* WHOLE TOWN ALREADY KNOWS YOUR SHIP'S DOWN."

"BUT H-HOW CAN HE *DO* THIS?! IF HE'S AN OUTLAW, WHY DOESN'T SOMEONE *REPORT* WHAT HE'S D-DOING?"

"*REPORT* IT? TO *WHO?* THE *REPUBLIC?*"

"AS IF THEY EVEN KNOW WHERE HORN STATION *IS.*"

"HEY!"

"HEY-- HEY, *WAKE UP!* THEY'RE *HERE!* THEY'RE DOWNSTAIRS!"

COME ON, YOU'VE GOTTA GO.

SHOULD'VE LET ME STAY WITH YOU LAST NIGHT.

THINK YOU COULD KEEP SOME BREAKFAST DOWN?

N-N-NO... I THINK I'M TOO N-NERVOUS FOR THAT, TOO.

NERVOUS OR NOT, I'VE SEEN HOW FAST YOU ARE. YOU CAN DO THIS.

GOOD LUCK.

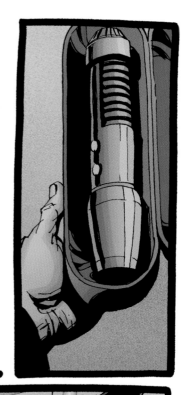

BAOOOM!

NON-LETHAL WOUNDS... STUN GRENADES...
STUN BEAMS... SHAPED CHARGES...
LIGHTSABERS...

...I HATE
JEDI
KNIGHTS.

Come on! We'll take my **hoverbuggy**!! It's got a harmonic resonance constripulator— if we can find *just* the right frequency, we should be able to identify the resonance from Max's *ORGAN!* We can track the Jawas using *THAT SIGNAL!!*

BRILLIANT!

JUMP!

ZOOOM!

Try to get a on the Org resonant field,

DRRRRRR

What the...?

That BOUNTY HUNTER is following us.

WHA Oh my go And a becaus what S about JAB

I **TOTALLY** disagree, by the way—I don't think of Jabba as a **BIG FAT SLUG** at all.

In fact, he's...

HANG ON!

ZOOM!

I'm gonna lose him in this rock formation!

104

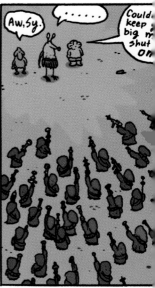

YAYY!! They're bringing out my VAN!

AND EVERY THING'S STI HERE!!

All righ

We... we *thank* you.

But please tell us-- why does a bounty hunter like you take the time to help us??

PSHHH

PSSS

Who ever said I was a *BOUNTY HUNTER*?! HUH-HUH! I'm a *harmonica* player, mr. Rebo!! Jawas can't *stand* the sound of a harmonica! me on the other hand-- I like it pretty good! Yup!! I've been following you for *days* now, trying to get up the nerve to ask you for an *audition!* I'm your biggest fan!!

I have everything you've ever recorded! Yup!! In fact I saw you *LIVE* once on Orto years ago & well, that was the first & most fantastic performance I've ever seen in my whole li like to fight

111

GOEN FOR A *RIDE*? HOO, IT'S A RELIEF. I TAUT ABEE YOU WAS *MAD* ABOUT SUMPTIN.

LIKE DAT LETTAL TTY AXYDENT WIT DA CITY SEWER SYSTEM.

OR DA OTOH GUNGA ZOO.

OR DA GASSER.

OR DA BOSS' HEYBLIBBER.

MY GUESS BOSS NASS ISA STILL *UPSET*, HUH?

YEP.

HMMM. MABEE I SHOULD DO SUMPTIN *NICE* FOR DA BOSS, LIKE... LIKE...

DO YOUSA KNOW HIS *CLOAK SIZE*?

TOO LATE-EST, JAR JAR, NO DO ANY GOOD.

SEE... BOSS NASS UN HIS *REP COUNCIL*... DEY *VOTE-ED*...

YOUSA REMEMBER WHAT DA BOSS SAY ABOUT DA *NOCOMBACKIE LAW*...?

TARPALS! LOOK OUT!

NO BE *INSULT-N*, MESA KNOW *ALL-N* YOUSA TRICKS, JAR JAR...

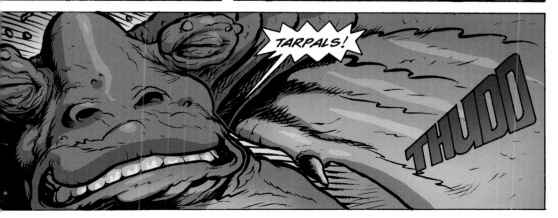

TARPALS!

THUDD

TANK DE GUDS YOUS OKEYDAY, TARPALS. WE WUZZA 'TACKED!

SPTH! WHA... WHAT HAPPENED?

MARSHOO UN HIS *PREP-COOKS*?!

YEAH... PITTY DUMB, DEM COMEN AFTER *YOUS*. FORTUNIT-LY, MY *SUBDUDE* DEM.

YOUS SUBDUDE DEM, HUH?

HEY, MESA NO LET *ANYBODY* MESS WIT MY PAL TARPALS... MESA MEAN, CAP'N TARPALS. NOSIR, MARSHOO HAD IT *COMEN*.

SO, ANYWAY, MESA TINKIN, MABEE ...IF NO TOO MUCH TROUBLE...YOUS MIGHT TELL DA *BOSS* HOW ME *HELP-ED* HAIR.

NORMALLY, ME SAY, "AW, NO MENTION IT, MESA JUST A *FRIEND* HEPPIN OUT *ANNUTTER FRIEND,*" NO BIG TING, RIGHT?

WHAT, JAR JAR?

DESE HANDI-CUFFS IS RILLY PINCHIN.

BOOT T WIT BOSS S BEIN *NO* PY WIT 1ESA...

TARPALS?

THE END

LET ME SEE IF I AM UNDERSTANDING YOU CORRECTLY, HOKAY?

LOVELY PLANET *OOTOOLA* FULL OF FISHFACES RULED BY PATRIARCH WHO IS KING AND PRIEST BOTH, SOME FISHFACES SAY PATRIARCH NOT PURE ENOUGH. KILL PATRIARCH. KILL WIFEY, SEIZE THRONE.

OOTOOLA PART OF REPUBLIC BUT GREAT SENATE DOES NOTHING, SAYS OOTOOLA PROBLEM INTERNAL. JEDI FRIENDS WANT HELP BUT NOT ALLOWED NEAR OOTOOLA BY NEW *PURIST* PATRIARCH.

"ONLY LITTLE FISHFACE PRINCESS LEFT FROM ORIGINAL FAMILY, PURISTS HUNT TO KILL HER, YOU WANT VILLIE SMUGGLE HER OFF PLANET, ALL CORRECT?"

DEAL WITH A DEMON

YES, WE HAVE FRIENDS AMONG THE DUR SABON WHO WILL PROTECT HER.

CAN YOU GET HER TO THEM?

BUT, YES, OF COURSE. FISHFACES DO GOOD TO COME TO *VILMARH GRAHRK*.

WHO BET THAN SMUGG GET LITTLE FIS GIRL OFF PLAN QUICK, EH

ONE--STOP CALLING THEM "FISHFACES." THEY DON'T APPRECIATE IT.

TWO--HOW DO WE KNOW WE CAN TRUST YOU?

AND YOU BE...?

NARADAN D'UL ATTENDANT AND CARE OF THE PRINCE

AH, THE *MISTRYL*. HEARD OF YOU, GOOD FIGHTER TYPES, YOU.

DO AS YOU LIKE. VILLIE GOING TO HIS SHIP.

COME QUICK-QUICK IF COME, PRINCESS AND MISTRYL ONLY.

LATER...

NT, SET COURSE FOR DUR SABON.

GREETINGS, PRINC FOOLOOKOOLA, IT IS WISH THAT YOU STAY US AS LONG AS YOU F COMFORTABLE ALTHO IS OUR HOPE YOU MA RETURN IN SAFETY T OWN WORLD SOO

REMEMBER-- YOU PROMISED TO PAY VILLIE DOUBLE.

YOU'RE LUCKY I HAVEN'T GUTTED YOU! I'M OPPOSED TO PAYING YOU ANYTHING!

THE LAW SAYS WHEN YOU DEAL WITH A DEMON YOU MUST EXPECT TO GET BURNED.

PAY THE DEMON HIS PRICE, AND IF HE EVER ENTERS OUR PRESENCE AGAIN --KILL HIM.

DON'T WORRY. VILLIE EVER GETS MIXED UP WITH FISHFACE AGAIN, VILLIE KILL HIMSELF.

THE

CLOUD CITY ON BESPIN.
A YEAR AFTER YAVIN.

I DOUBLED YOUR BET *CALRISSIAN!* READY TO QUIT?

TOO RICH FOR YOU, eh? CAN'T HANDLE A MEN'S GAME OF *SABACC,* eh?

NOT AT ALL, DREBBLE! I'LL COVER YOU--

--AND I'LL ADD ANOTHER TWENTY-FIVE THOUSAND! CAN *YOU* FOLLOW?

YOU CAN'T DO THIS TO ME! LET ME SEE THOSE!

Lady Luck

FLUMP

ARE YOU ENJOYING YOUR STAY WITH US, SIR?

Hm? OH, YES, LOBOT, I AM.

ANOTHER GAME OPPORTUNITY HAS PRESENTED ITSELF. WOULD SIR CARE TO TRY?

SURE, WHY NOT? I'M ON A WINNING STREAK!

BARON RAYNOR EXPRESSED A WISH TO PLAY AGAINST YOU.

THE BARON RAYNOR? *DOMINIC* RAYNOR?

THE BARON ADMINISTRATOR OF BESPIN, YES.

I THOUGHT THE OFFICIALS WERE PROHIBITED FROM PARTICIPATING IN THE GAMES.

BUT WHO'S TO STOP THEM, SIR?

THE BARON AWAITS YOU IN THE ECCLESSIS FIGG ROOM, SIR, IN THE BACK.

132

LANDO CALRISSIAN... YOU BELIEVE YOU CAN *BEAT* ME?

WINNING IS SECONDARY, BARON. I JUST ENJOY THE GAMES.

I ONLY ENJOY THOSE I WIN--

--AND I EXPECT TO *ENJOY* THIS ONE!

134

YOU [WI]TCH TO RAISE [TH]E STAKES BUT [YO]U ARE RUNNING [OU]T OF CASH... [A]M I RIGHT?

WILL YOU ACCEPT A SHIP?

THE COBRA?

CERTAINLY, WHY NOT?

HE HAS A SABACC!

WHO HAS?

LANDO!

WHAT DOES RAYNOR HAVE?

HERE'S THE TITLE FOR THE COBRA.

AND HERE'S AN IDIOT'S ARRAY!

IT WAS A PLEASURE, CALRISSIAN! TOO BAD YOU HAD TO LOSE!

A MOMENT, SIR, IF YOU WOULD.

SOMEONE'S BEEN USING A SKIFTER TO RIG THE GAME.

HOW DARE YOU ASSUME I WOULD DO SUCH A THING?

I NEVER ASSUME, BARON. THE DEALER HAS ONE.

YOU!

I APOLOGIZE, SIR... I... IT'S... I... DREBBLE PAID ME!

DREBBLE!

I WANTED TO HELP YOU, BARON! WITH A SMALL REVENGE IN THERE FOR MYSELF... I... I...

AAA!

136

LOOK HIM UP! I'LL DO SOMETHING *UNPLEASANT* TO HIM LATER.

WHAT ABOUT THE GAME?

NOTHING IN THE RULES SAYS I SHOULD RETURN THE WINNINGS BECAUSE SOMEBODY *ELSE* CHEATED!

TERRIBLY SORRY, CALRISSIAN!

A MOMENT, SIR, IF YOU WOULD.

AGAIN? YOU'RE BECOMING POSITIVELY *CHEEKY*, LOBOT!

AN ANONYMOUS GIFT HAS ARRIVED FOR YOU, SIR.

A *GIFT*?

FIVE MILLION CREDITS. FROM PEOPLE WHO WANT THIS MATCH TO CONTINUE.

PLAY, CALRISSIAN. WHAT ARE YOU WAITING FOR?

FOUR MILLION ON THE TABLE. THINKING OF RAISING, CALRISSIAN?

YOU HAVE *NO IDEA* WHAT I'M THINKING, RAYNOR.

ALL OF THIS *PLUS* MY STARSHIP LOT ON NAR SHADDAA-- *AGAINST THE CLOUD CITY!*

AHA HAHA HA HA

A *SCRAP LOT* AGAINST MY CITY? WHAT A CLOWN YOU ARE, CALRISSIAN!

A *STARSHIP* WITH THREE SURRONIAN FARSTARS IN IT. *PRE-EMPIRE* SURRONIAN FARSTARS!

WHAT ARE... THESE PRE-EMPIRE THINGS, DOMINIC?

COLLECTOR'S ITEMS... FIRST CLASS.

YOU'RE *ON*, CALRISSIAN!

I SORT OF *HOPED* YOU'D SAY THAT!

SABACC.

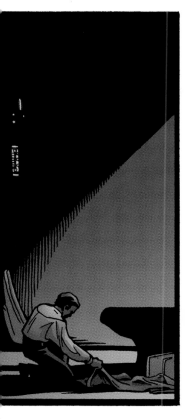

LOBOT?

SIR?

WHAT WAS THIS ALL ABOUT?

SIR?

THE ANONYMOUS GIFT? THE RIGHT CARD AT THE RIGHT MOMENT? SUCH LUCK SIMPLY DOES NOT EXIST?

IT DOES NOW, SIR. IT NEEDED A LITTLE HELP, OF COURSE--

IS WARE, RE.

AND YOUR ENHANCED BRAIN.

AND THE MONEY?

FIFTY THOUSAND WORKERS. HERE AND IN THE MINES. NONE LIKED WHAT RAYNOR DID TO THE CITY.

145

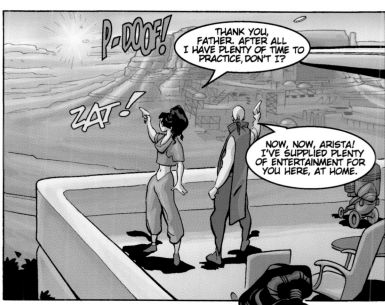

NICE ANKLE BRACELET.

P-DOOF!

TOO BAD IT'S NOT AROUND YOUR NECK, UNCLE SETH.

ZAT!

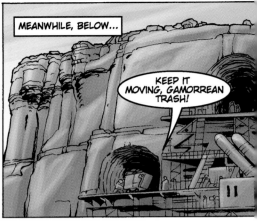

MEANWHILE, BELOW...

KEEP IT MOVING, GAMORREAN TRASH!

FASTER! UNLESS YOU'D LIKE EXTRA TIME ADDED TO YOUR SENTENCE!

HEY, PIGSNOUT! YOU'D BETTER WATCH YOUR BACK!!

GRISSOM PONDERS WHAT HE HAS DONE TO DESERVE SUCH MISFORTUNE.

"BY TOMORROW, LORN KABUL WILL BE DEAD!"

...SEWHERE...

GRIEF STRICKEN OVER HER FATHER'S DEATH, ARISTA HAS REMAINED SILENT SINCE REGAINING CONSCIOUSNESS.

IN HER HEART SHE KNOWS HER UNCLE SETH MUST BE RESPONSIBLE.

...SOM WORRIES TIME ...INNING OUT.

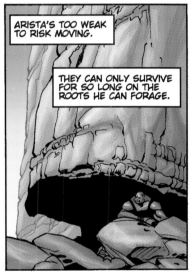

ARISTA'S TOO WEAK TO RISK MOVING.

THEY CAN ONLY SURVIVE FOR SO LONG ON THE ROOTS HE CAN FORAGE.

AND THERE'S THE MATTER OF ARISTA'S TRACKING DEVICE...

...STRATED, GRISSOM ONCE ...N STRUGGLES TO REMOVE ...STUBBORN BRACELET.

SO INTENT IS GRISSOM HE FAILS TO NOTICE...

...A SECRET OBSERVER.

157

THE SUN SETS. THE DESERT COOLS. NIGHT SCAVENGERS ARE ON THE PROWL.

THE SIGNAL POINTS OVER THAT RIDGE!

LOOK...A FIRE LIGHT!

SLOW...QUIET NOW.

WE FOUND HER.

ME WAKE HER WITH A KISS!

WHA--?!

AAAAHHH!!!

RROAARR!

159

THE KABUL ESTATE.

IT SEEMS MY UNCLE HAS ACQUIRED SOME NEW IMPERIAL FRIENDS.

TEK, YOU KNOW WHAT TO DO. GOOD LUCK.

I BID YOU GOODNIGHT, KABUL. I MUST GO ATTEND TO THE DEPARTMENT OF MY TROOPERS.

BY MORNING KABUL ESTATE WILL BE TOTALLY OCCUPIED AND SECURED.

VERY GOOD, HARSH. VERY GOOD.

BEST NOT TELL HARSH ABOUT ARISTA.

I'M SURE SHE'LL TURN UP SOON ENOUGH.

GREETINGS UNCLE.

ARISTA!

THANK THE STARS YOU'RE ALIVE!

CUT THE ACT [UN]CLE, I KNOW [YO]U KILLED MY [FAT]HER! NOW WITH [TH]E EMPIRE ON [Y]OUR SIDE, I CAN'T GET THE MINES BACK.

BUT AT [L]EAST I'LL HAVE THE [SA]TISFACTION [OF] WATCHING [YO]U BEG FOR [Y]OUR LIFE.

ARISTA, YOU CAN'T BE SERIOUS!

DEADLY SERIOUS, UNCLE.

GO AHEAD, ARISTA. THIS ISN'T THE SAME AS SHOOTING A SKEET.

YOU'RE RIGHT UNCLE, I'M NO KILLER.

MY FRIEND ON THE OTHER HAND...

NO! NO! I BEG YOU, DON'T KILL ME!

YOU'LL LIVE...FOR NOW!

DON'T FAINT UNCLE, I WANT YOU TO SEE SOMETHING.

IN AN INSTANT, VADER REALIZES HIS MISTAKE.

TSSSSHH·K·K·K

HE MISTOOK THE AURA HE FELT FROM TARK TO BE THE USUAL ATTITUDE OF KILLERS WHEN, IN ACTUALITY, IT WAS HUNGER FOR PREY.

BUT HE DOES NOT LET THOUGHTS OF RECRIMINATION FOG HIS MIND.

THE ATTACK IS FAST AND PRECISE. TOO LINEAR AN ATTACK CAN BE EASILY AVOIDED.

ATTACKS, LIKE PEOPLE, CAN BE DECEIVING. NOW VADER HAS HIS ANSWER.

AS HE FALLS WITHIN DEATH'S GRASP, VADER REACHES INTO HIS OPPONENT'S MIND.

HE USES HIS MENTAL ABILITIES, HOPING TO TAKE CONTROL OF HIS FOE, PUSHING PAST THE HATRED THAT POSSESSES TARK.

NO! NOT TARK, BUT STAUZ CZYCZ. WHO IS THIS MAN? AS QUICKLY AS THE QUESTION FORMS, VADER IS PULLED FURTHER INTO THE ASSASSIN'S MIND.

STAUZ WAS A SOLDIER ON A WORLD WHICH PALPATINE HAD CHOSEN TO MAKE AN EXAMPLE OF.

HE FOUGHT FOR HIS HOME AND FAMILY.

BUT THE WAR ROBBED HIM OF HIS YOUTHFUL DREAMS AND HIS FAMILY.

YAAARGH!

WELCOMING THE DARKNESS OF HIS LOSS, STAUZ SERVED UP HIS OWN BODY IN EXCHANGE FOR REVENGE.

BUT THIS DEAL HAD A LOOPHOLE THROUGH WHICH STAUZ'S WISH COULD ESCAPE AND HIS SACRIFICE WOULD COME TO NAUGHT.

VMMMMM!

THE FULL EXTENT OF STAUZ'S WRATH EXPLODES INTO VADER'S INTELLECT.

THE FORCE OF THIS FURY DRIVES VADER FROM STAUZ'S BRAIN AND PARALYZES THE PAIR IN A FIERCE EMBRACE.

THIS REPRIEVE PASSES AND VADER USES HIS TELEKINETIC SKILLS TO KILL THE POWER TO STAUZ'S IMPLANTED FORCE-FIELD GENERATOR.

VAAAAASHHHH!!

VADER PUTS AN END TO STAUZ'S EXISTENCE, AS QUICKLY AND BRUTALLY AS HE HAS ENDED THE LIVES OF SO MANY BEFORE.

YET, NEVER BEFORE HAS VADER FACED A FOE SO DEDICATED TO RAGE, SO PREPARED AND SCHOOLED IN THE DEALING OF DEATH, AN ADVERSARY SO MUCH LIKE HIMSELF,

SOME TIME LATER...

MOST OF THE DAMAGE THAT STAUZ HAD DEALT WAS ONLY TO VADER'S ARMOR AND WAS QUICKLY REPAIRED.

HE CAN FEEL THE STRENGTH RETURNING TO HIS LIMBS, THE BREATH TO HIS LUNGS, AND MORE... HE CAN SMELL THE FEAR OF THOSE AROUND HIM. HIS SELF-CONFIDENCE HAS NOT BEEN SHAKEN.

LORD VADER, SIR, THERE IS A MESSAGE FOR YOU FROM BESPIN,

I WILL RECEIVE THE MESSAGE ON THE BRIDGE,

LORD VADER RISES FROM THIS BATTLE STRONGER THAN BEFORE, AND YET HIS ARMOR HAS BEEN BREACHED... AND HIS MIND TURNS TO THINGS THAT HE HAS NOT CONSIDERED IN MANY YEARS,

HE WONDERS ABOUT A DEAD MAN WHO LOST HIS CHILDREN AND SACRIFICED HIS HUMANITY FOR HIS NEED FOR REVENGE.

DARTH VADER WONDERS ABOUT A FATHER WHO DIED MORE OF A MACHINE THAN A MAN.

END

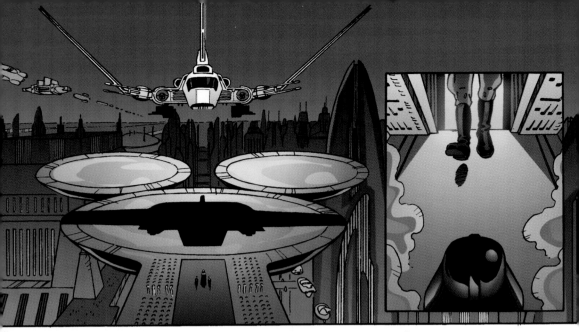

GREETINGS, MOFF TARKIN.

WE ARE HONORED BY YOUR PRESENCE, AND THAT OF YOUR GUES--

YES, YES, SPLENDID. THANK YOU VERY MUCH.

IF MEMORY SERVES ME, I BELIEVE WE GO THIS WAY.

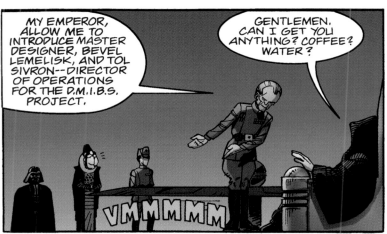

WATER.

WATER.

WHAT KIND OF WATER?

AQUILIE.

...I'LL TAKE A COFFEE.

OKAY, TARKIN, LET'S CUT THROUGH THE FORMALITIES, I RECEIVED YOUR ADVANCE COMMUNICATION AND HAVE LOOKED OVER THE PLANS.

ALTHOUGH I FIND IT MOST IMPRESSIVE...

...THERE ARE STILL A FEW MINOR DETAILS I WISH TO GO OVER WITH YOU.

NO CREAM.

MILK

GISH!

BUT OF COURSE, MY EMPEROR, WHAT IS IT THAT TROUBLES YOU EXACTLY?

WELL, FOR STARTERS, THE NAME, D.M.I.B.S.? THAT DOESN'T REALLY STRIKE TERROR INTO YOUR HEART, DOES IT?

MY EMPEROR, IT'S SIMPLY THE ACRONYM FOR--DEEP-SPACE MOBILE IMPERIAL BATTLE STATION. ALL PROJECTS ARE NAMED THUS FOR EASIER RECORD KEEPING.

NO, I UNDERSTAND, BUT THAT NAME WOULD JUST LOOK TOO BUSY ON ANY OF OUR STATIONERY. I NEED SOMETHING STRAIGHT AND TO THE POINT.

THE PLANET KILLER.

NOT THAT STRAIGHT AND TO THE POINT, I WANT EPIC.

phft

DEATH FROM ABOVE?

SUN BLOCKER!!

TITANIC?

HOW ABOUT THE DEATH STAR?

OH, PLEASE!

YOU CAN'T SERIOUS

NO. I LIKE IT, IT HAS A KIND OF DUPLICITY TO IT -- ONE OF BOTH HOPE AND TERROR.

OKAY, LET'S GET DOWN TO SOME DESIGN SPECS.

BZZZ-Z-T

YES, MY EMPEROR.

I'M EXCEEDINGLY SORRY, MY EMPEROR. MY DAUGHTER MUST HAVE TAKEN ONE OF MY HOLO-PROJECTORS BY MISTAKE.

BZZZ-T

THE DEATH STAR IS 120 KILOMETERS IN DIAMETER. IT HAS A QUADANIUM STEEL HULL, A CLASS 4 HYPERDRIVE, FIVE THOUSAND IMPERIAL TURBO BATTERIES, FIVE THOUSAND HEAVY-TURBO BATTERIES, 768 TRACTOR BEAMS.

OKAY. STOP RIGHT THERE.

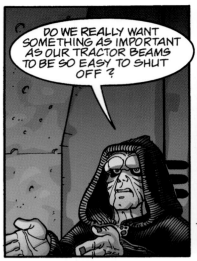

DO WE REALLY WANT SOMETHING AS IMPORTANT AS OUR TRACTOR BEAMS TO BE SO EASY TO SHUT OFF ?

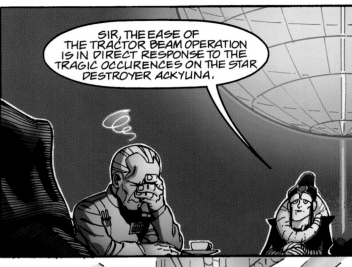

SIR, THE EASE OF THE TRACTOR BEAM OPERATION IS IN DIRECT RESPONSE TO THE TRAGIC OCCURENCES ON THE STAR DESTROYER ACKYUNA.

MY EMPEROR, NOT ALL STORM-TROOPERS ARE AS SMART AS WE WOULD LIKE TO THINK. ANYTHING WE CAN DO TO SIMPLIFY THEIR DAY WILL BE BENEFICIAL IN THE LONG RUN.

TRUE, TRUE,

WHAT ABOUT THESE BOTTOMLESS PITS. WOL IT BE TOO MUCH TO ASI FOR SOME SAFETY RAILS I MEAN, I'M RUTHLESS, B I GOTTA WALK THESE HAL TOO, AND MY BALANCE AI WHAT IT USED TO BE.

IT'S NOT TOO MUCH TO ASK, AS LONG AS YOU DON'T MIND AN OVERALL BUDGET INCREASE OF 36%.

OH, IN THAT CASE, I'LL JUST BE CAREFUL.

WHENEVER I'M ON THIS THING, WANT YOU WITH ME AT ALL TIME THE LAST THING I NEED IS FOR SOME GUY TO SNEAK UP BEHIN ME AND THROW ME INTO ONE OF THESE PITS.

YES, MY MASTER.

184

WHERE'S THE PORT LOCATED?

MID-HEMISPHERIC EQUATORIAL TRENCH.

WHAT IS THE MINIMUM SAFETY REQUIREMENT FOR VENTILATION?

WE CAN GO AS SMALL AS TWO METERS.

HOW MANY CANNONS LINE THE TRENCH?

250 STANDARD, 250 ION.

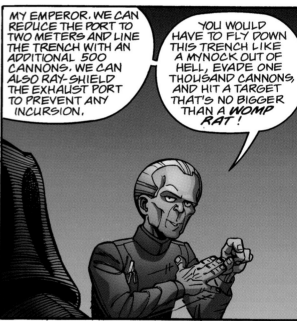

MY EMPEROR, WE CAN REDUCE THE PORT TO TWO METERS AND LINE THE TRENCH WITH AN ADDITIONAL 500 CANNONS. WE CAN ALSO RAY-SHIELD THE EXHAUST PORT TO PREVENT ANY INCURSION.

YOU WOULD HAVE TO FLY DOWN THIS TRENCH LIKE A MYNOCK OUT OF HELL, EVADE ONE THOUSAND CANNONS, AND HIT A TARGET THAT'S NO BIGGER THAN A *WOMP RAT*!

TRUST ME, THERE IS NO ONE IN THE GALAXY WHO COULD MAKE SUCH A SHOT.

AHEM.

EXCEPT, OF COURSE, LORD VADER.

186

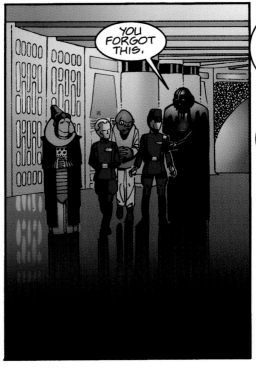

YOU FORGOT THIS.

YOU CAN'T JUST LEAVE THESE THINGS LYING AROUND. I'D HATE TO HAVE THEM FALL INTO THE WRONG HANDS AND HAVE YOU LOOK BAD IN FRONT OF OUR EMPEROR, *GRAND* MOFF.

YES, OF COURSE, TH-THANK YOU, LORD VADER.

MY PLEASURE.

THE END

LUCAS + KEVIN '00

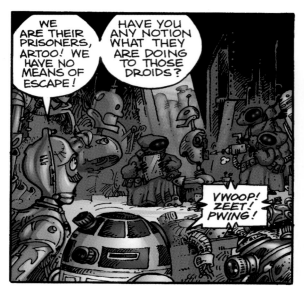

THIS IS DOUBTLESSLY THE SOURCE OF THE UNREGISTERED, UNTRACEABLE PARTS THAT HAVE FLOODED THE DROID TRADE AS OF LATE...

'IP! 'IP! 'ET!

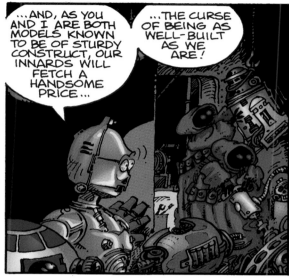

...AND, AS YOU AND I ARE BOTH MODELS KNOWN TO BE OF STURDY CONSTRUCT, OUR INNARDS WILL FETCH A HANDSOME PRICE...

...THE CURSE OF BEING AS WELL-BUILT AS WE ARE!

'WOOT! 'ZEET! 'VEEEET!

SAY THAT AGAIN! I DID NOT HEAR YOU!

OH, WAIT! I KNOW WHAT YOU ARE SAYING...

YOU FEEL WE SHOULD ATTEMPT AN ESCAPE AT OUR FIRST OPPORTUNITY...

WELL, I CANNOT ARGUE WITH THAT! HAVE YOU ANY IDEA HOW TO ACCOMPLISH IT?

'WEET! 'OOP! 'OOP! 'EEP!

I AM SKEPTICAL! DO YOU TRULY THINK THAT WILL WORK?

BUT YOU ARE RIGHT! IF WE DO NOT ACT WITH DISPATCH, PARTS OF US WILL WIND UP IN SOMEONE'S GUIDANCE MATRIX OR HEATING SYSTEM...

...OR EVEN--DARE I THINK IT?--SOME PIECE OF COOKING APPARATUS!

BEEPADEEP! BEEPADEEP!

THE END

BIGG GIZZ & SPIKER IN
SAND BLASTED

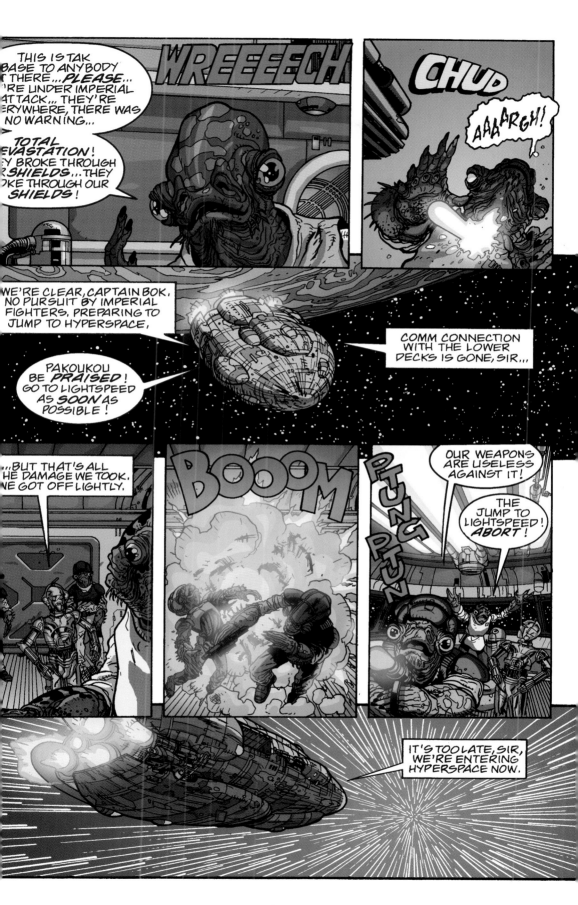

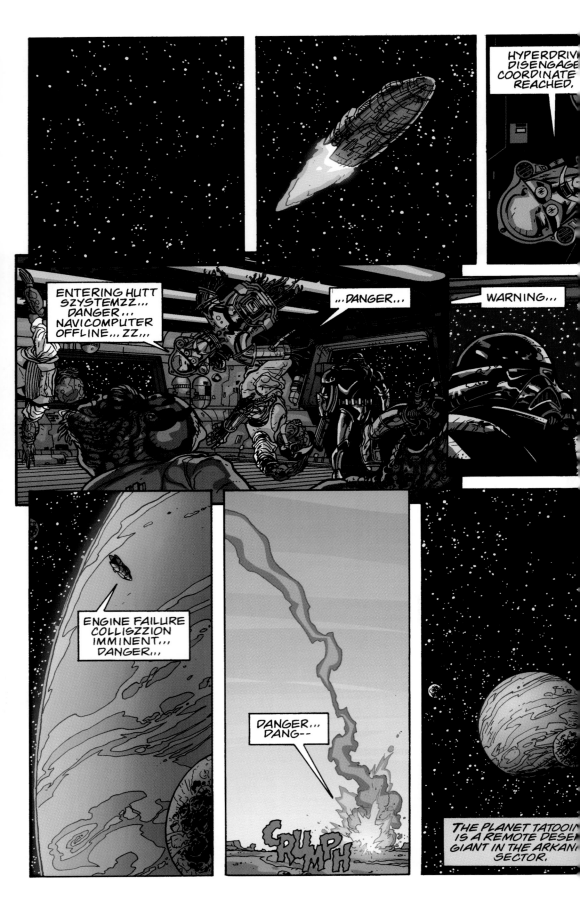

A WRECKED SPACECRAFT CAN LIE BURIED IN ITS SHIFTING SANDS FOR **YEARS**. GIVEN TIME, THOUGH, NATIVE SCAVENGERS WILL LIKELY UNCOVER IT.

EVEN THOUGH SOME THINGS SHOULD BEST BE *LEFT* BURIED...

RUBUMBLRUMBLBRURBL

RURBURLRUMBLRRUBML

RUUMBLBUMBRL...

HUH? WASSAH? WHA--

LAAAGH!

ICKKEE *KLEPTI B'AY!* KEETA MIK!

HE SAYS HIS NAME IS *KLEPTI,* OF THE B'AY TRIBE. HE'S *WARNING* US...

< MY TRIBE CAME UPON A WRECK OUT BEYON THE GREAT DUNES, A TREASURE, WE THOUGHT, B REALLY A *CURSE.* >

< INSIDE DWELLED A *MONSTER* OF TH UGLY WHITE CLAN FR THE SKY. A *DROID* O A KIND UNSEEN...>

HUH?!

THUNK

O-OH, NO! IT'S AN *IMPERIAL BATTLE DROID!* WE'RE *FINISHED!*

WAIT, I SEEN *THESE.* IT'S AN *IG97* UNIT!...

POOOF

...AN THEY AIN'T *SCARY.*

I DUNNO WHAT YOU JUST BEEN TOLD, BUT THE *EMPIRE* NEVER MADE NO *BATTLE DROIDS.*

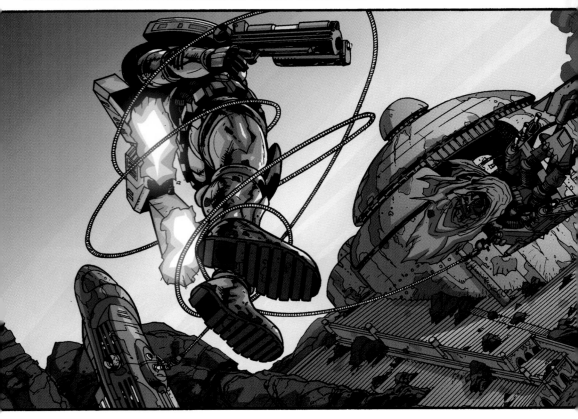

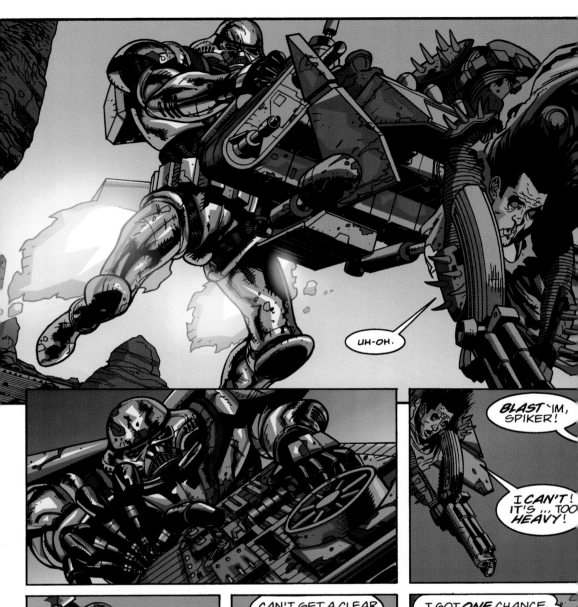

UH-OH.

BLAST 'IM, SPIKER!

I CAN'T! IT'S ... TOO HEAVY!

CAN'T GET A CLEAR SHOT! THIS IS BAD!

I GOT ONE CHANCE, CUT THE THRUSTERS DEAD...

...OR I'M DEAD *MYSELF!*

KER-ASHHH

YOU OKAY, BUDDY?

UNPH! I'VE TAKEN *WORSE* SPILLS,

WREEEEEH

WELL, I'LL BE...

...THEY AIN'T SO USELESS EITHER!

MAYBE NOT, BUT THAT 'CRAWLER'S HAD IT! SHE'S GONNA BLOW!

RUN!

CHUKEE *CHUWEEFA* JUK!...

...OT JUDATEEPA KIKIDEE! WUCKWABA *CHOOB* TEE

HUUUHN.

UHH, WHAT'D HE SAY?

WELL, MASTER SPIKER, HE SAID HERE'S YOUR *HELMET* AND, ER...

...WE ARE NOW HIS CLAN AND HE WILL FOLLOW US FOREVER.

GREAT, *ANOTHER* FEEB TO DRAG AROUND.

HEHEH. RUSTBUCKET BLOWED UP *REAL* GOOD!

217

THIS PIECE OF JUNK SAVED OUR *HIDES*, AN' HE'S THE ONLY ONE OF US WHO'S STILL GOT A *BLASTER*.

THANKS TO *YOU*. YA HAD TO *THROW* THE JAWA'S *AWAY*! NICE GOIN', *GENIUS*.

SO, JUST KEEP THE *GUN* AND LEAVE THE DROID *HERE*!

BICKADIBEE NISEVENA! JUD WEETO NEFOODA! A TUTA GOK GOOFO!

KLEPTI SAYS IG97 IS FINE MERCHANDISE AND WILL FETCH A GOOD PRICE AT THE NEAREST SETTLEMENT.

GOOD PRICE?! WE'RE *SWOOP SCUM*! VICIOUS *THUGS*! WE DON'T TRADE *NOTHIN'*!

SO, UH, HOW MUCH DOES HE THINK WE COULD *GET*?

WOK, WOOPA CHIGA *CHOOT*.

HUH?

"WELL, HE SAYS..."

THE END